Chapter One

This story begins on a dark and stormy night. Well, actually, that's not strictly true. It was definitely dark, but not exactly stormy. Though it probably should have been. For this is a tale of dreadful villainy. Of foul play, wickedness and shameful wrongdoings. It's the story of a man who ought to have known better.

And that man's name is Ron the robber.

It all takes place in the sleepy town of Scrubbley, on a quiet leafy road called Wayward Crescent. Most of the people who live in this Crescent are perfectly ordinary, respectable folks. But as some of you will know, the house towards the end, at number 42, is owned by a woman called Elizabeth Pennykettle – 'Liz' to her neighbours, 'Mum' to her nine-year-old daughter, Lucy.

Now, though she's respectable, Liz is not entirely ordinary. She makes dragons, clay dragons, which she sells on the market. There's

Chris d'Lacey

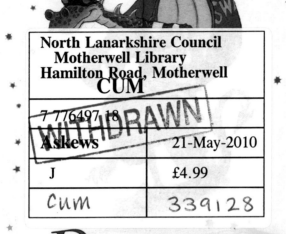

The Dragons of Wayward Crescent

GRABBER

Illustrated by Adam Stower

ORCHARD BOOKS

nothing very strange about that, of course. But every now and then, when a magical mood inspires her, Liz makes a special kind of dragon. One that might look like a normal solid sculpture, but is in fact real. Very, very real.

This is how it was on the night that Ron the robber broke into Liz's house. She had just made a new special dragon. A handsome young male. At that time his special abilities were not known. And he had no name.

Liz had left him on her potter's turntable, in her workroom upstairs which she called the Dragons' Den, while she and Lucy had gone out for the evening. The new dragon was in the care of a female called Guinevere. Guinevere was Liz's personal dragon and she was *very* special indeed. It was Guinevere's job to 'awaken' the young dragons when they were made. How she did it was a secret, and the details are not to be written down here. All that matters for the moment is that the dragon on the turntable could blink and blow smoke rings and swish his tail. He was eager to test his wings as well. For there was lots to explore in the Dragons' Den. The window that looked out onto the garden, for instance. And the shelves of fascinating dragon sculptures. But

Guinevere had spoken firmly to him in dragontongue, telling him he must await Liz's return before trying out his flying skills. Young dragons, she had said, had much to learn.

So, there we have it. The scene is set. As the sun goes down and the Dragons' Den falls into dusky shadow, picture the young dragon sitting and waiting, drumming his claws on the wooden turntable,

warming the air with a *hrrr* now and then.

Then, suddenly, his ears prick up. From somewhere far below he has heard a sound. A gentle crash. A sharp sort of tinkle. He is too young to know about the layout of the house, or that the sound is a small pane of glass breaking in the kitchen door. But he sits up eagerly, expectantly, keenly, wondering if this means his mistress is coming.

Just then, however, another young dragon swoops into the den. This is Gruffen. He is a guard dragon, made to protect Lucy Pennykettle from danger. But Lucy is not here. She is in no danger. But Gruffen is concerned that the house might be.

As he lands on the table next to Guinevere he tells her what he has seen downstairs. He was on the kitchen table when the glass was broken. He saw a gloved hand fiddle through the hole and turn the key which was sitting in the lock. He saw the door open and a man step in. Not Henry, the Pennykettles' next door neighbour. A stranger. A stranger dressed like the night. Sturdy black boots. Black jacket. Black hat. A stranger carrying a flashing torch.

Guinevere urges him to search through his book. (Gruffen has a book which he always carries with him, a kind of manual of dragon procedures.) By the light of Guinevere's violet flame, he looks up the word '*strangers*'. The new young dragon leans forward to watch. This is very exciting! He wonders if life here is always like this?

There is an entry in the book, but it is not very helpful. *In the presence of strangers, act solid*, it says. This is a rule all the special dragons know – except for those just born, of course.

There is a creak on the landing. A footstep. Two. Light breaks at steep angles into the Den. Gruffen and Guinevere immediately turn solid, forgetting that the youngster doesn't know what to do.

A figure steps in. He is short. A little brawny. Stubble on the fatty parts of his chin. The light twists and burrs around the shelves, making

soft glints as it catches on the ears
and tails of clay.

"Well, well, what 'ave we 'ere?"
the figure says. A man. Soft-spoken.
Quite elderly, perhaps. With slightly
yellow teeth. And slightly fishy
breath.

The light flips again, towards the table. It passes over Guinevere. It passes over Gruffen. But when it hits the new dragon, he sits up and *hrrrs*…

"What the—?" The light jerks back and stays there for a moment. Then it grows steadily big once more.

The new dragon flaps his wings.

"Well, dust my brain, you *moved*," the voice croaks.

The young dragon paddles his feet. He can't understand the soft grunts the man is making, but he's sure he'll learn in time. A finger comes forward and prods his snout.

Not quite the greeting the dragon was expecting, but contact, just the same. Now he can't resist. He has got to fly. With a flutter that the stranger would have struggled to see, the little dragon lands in the palm of his hand.

"Stone the crows! I'm 'aving you," says the man.

And he drops the young dragon into a sack.

Into a world of dastardly robbery.

Into a seedy life of crime…

Chapter Two

"They took the dragon?!" Lucy's pale face froze in shock. "They burgled our house and stole a dragon?!"

"Mmm. Strangely, nothing else was taken," said Liz.

After what seemed like a pause

long enough to boil an egg, Lucy pulled a strand of straw-coloured hair from her mouth and added, "Mum, I don't care about anything else! That dragon's *special*. He'll be frightened. He won't know what to do. How are we going to get him back?"

Her mother leaned against the worktop and hummed. "There's no need to panic—"

"'Course there is!" Lucy shouted. "He doesn't know the rules. If he starts *doing* things, the person who took him will know he's real! What *does* he do, anyway? What kind of dragon is he? Did you give him a name? Will we have to move house?"

"Calm down," said Liz. "One question at a time. No, I didn't call him anything, and he won't start showing any special ability until someone does give him a name – and even then it would have to begin with a 'G'. It's highly unlikely that the person who took him will do either of those things."

"But if they *did*," persisted Lucy, "then what?"

"Well, the dragon might begin to follow the habits of that person. Like animals do sometimes when they're reared by different mothers."

Lucy wrinkled her nose.

Liz tried to explain. "Imagine an orphaned baby duckling had been rescued by a wolf. After a time, the duck would start acting like a wolf."

"Uh?" went Lucy, momentarily distracted by the thought of a duckling howling at the moon. Then her eyes widened as she understood properly. "You mean the dragon will become a robber?!"

Liz sighed heavily and folded her arms. "It won't come to that. I agree the dragon might move around, but the robber will struggle to see him. Human eyes aren't really quick enough to follow them, unless you're special – like us."

To Lucy's relief, Liz reached out and hugged her. "Don't worry, we'll find our dragon. Sooner or later he's going to get fretful and start putting out some sort of call. The listener is on full alert. He'll pick up any traces. We should be able to track it fairly easily."

Lucy glanced at the dragon on top of the fridge. Its big delicate ears were already turning like radar dishes.

"It might be best," Liz continued, "if we don't tell anyone what's happened."

"Oh," said Lucy. Her shoulders stiffened.

"Ah. I take it that means you've already rung Melanie?"

Melanie was Lucy's favourite friend. Lucy blushed and shook her head. "No, but I did tell *someone*…"

At that point, the tall gawky figure of Henry Bacon appeared on the other side of the kitchen door. He was dressed from neck to toe in a one-piece white overall. In his right hand he was carrying a leather holdall. Without asking permission, he put a gloved hand through the broken pane of glass, turned the key and let himself in, just like Ron the robber had the night before.

"Thought so. Common mistake, Mrs P. Key left on view. Open invitation to a felon, is that."

A puff of hot air came out of Liz's mouth. "I take it this is the 'someone'?" she asked.

"Sorry," Lucy said in a quiet little voice.

Liz moved her aside. "All right, I'll deal with it. Henry, why are you dressed in that ridiculous outfit? You look like a milk-flavoured lollipop."

Henry held up a hand. "Not too close, Mrs P. You'll tarnish the crime scene."

"It's my kitchen," Liz said, her voice sounding ominous. "I'll 'tarnish' it as much as I like."

"No, no." Henry was adamant. "We need to gather forensic evidence."

"Foreign what?" said Lucy.

"Forensics, child. Stand away. This could be messy."

Without further ado, Henry opened his holdall and produced, of all things, a bag of flour and a paintbrush. To Liz and Lucy's astonishment (and even Gruffen's, who flew stealthily forward to take a closer look) Henry dipped the brush into the flour and began to 'paint' it over the door frame.

"Henry, what on earth are you doing?!"

"Dusting for fingerprints, Mrs P. They'll show up in the flour."

"I'll dust you," she barked, "if you don't stop that."

She reached out to grab the paintbrush from him. But Henry turned suddenly and the movement threw a cloud of flour over Gruffen. The guard dragon sneezed and blew most of it back into Henry's face.

Momentarily blinded, Henry jerked to one side and put his elbow through another pane of glass in the door. The smash made Lucy squeal. As a result, Gruffen reacted as any guard dragon would. He hurred and sent out a jet of flame. The tip of the flame singed Henry's wrist. Henry yelped and threw the bag of flour upwards. It hit the ceiling and split wide open, coating the entire kitchen in fluffy white powder.

It was perhaps a good job that the front door bell rang at that moment, for Liz was on the verge of doing something unspeakable to her meddling neighbour. "OH!" she went and stomped down the hall. She yanked the door open.

Two gentlemen in ties and mackintoshes were there. The older one was wearing a battered trilby hat. He raised an experienced eyebrow. "Is this a bad time, madam?" He nodded at Liz's hair. Her beautiful red curls were peppered white.

"Accident – in the kitchen. What do you want?"

The older man showed an identity card. "I'm Detective Inspector Bumble

and this is my junior, Sergeant Beale."

"Bee?" Liz said. "Bumble and Bee?"

"Beale," said the younger man, leaning forward politely.

Liz worked up a small smile. A fine avalanche of flour fell from her hair.

"Your neighbour, a Mr Bacon, reported a robbery. May we come in?"

Liz tapped her foot. "It's nothing serious."

Inspector Bumble gave a well-worn smile. "I think we should be the judge of that, Mrs…?"

"Pennykettle."

"Thank you. There have been a number of burglaries in Wayward Crescent recently. This villain is becoming quite a nuisance. An interesting nuisance at that."

"Interesting? In what way?" asked Liz.

"He only steals certain kinds of trinkets," said Beale.

"Not dragons?" said Liz.

The two policemen looked at one another. Inspector Bumble nodded. "That would fit the pattern. This gentleman of the night is like a magpie, Mrs Pennykettle. He likes to collect up shiny objects: jewellery, gem stones – and on the odd occasion, toys…"

Chapter Three

Liz led the policemen through to the kitchen, warning them to watch where they put their feet.

"Ah, good," said Henry. "The cavalry's arrived."

Inspector Bumble assessed the situation with a practised gaze. He

28

ran a finger over the worktop, making a curving smear in the flour. Then he unwrapped a soft mint and popped it into his mouth. "You can leave the detecting to us now, sir. Perhaps you ought to take up cooking, instead?"

"Nonsense," said Henry, pointing to the door frame. "I've uncovered a print!"

Sergeant Beale crouched down and squinted at it. "That's not human. Looks more like a bird."

"Probably a dragon," Liz said fractiously.

Inspector Bumble chewed his mint. He glanced at Gruffen and the timing dragon, Gauge, who was sitting by the cooker. Both had turned solid, of course. "You mentioned dragons on the doorstep. Has one gone missing?"

"Yes!" said Lucy, unable to stop herself.

Liz rolled her eyes to the ceiling. So much for not telling anyone.

The weight of the law now turned towards Lucy. "And what can you tell us about it, Miss?" Inspector Bumble cracked his knuckles and waited.

"He's very young," Lucy said, aware that she was blushing.

"He?"

"It's a boy."

"I see," said Bumble. "Make a note of this, Beale." The sergeant pulled a notebook out of his pocket. "Was it valuable?"

"Mrs P. flogs her wares on her market stall," said Henry. "Fifteen pounds each. Discount for two."

The inspector pursed his lips. "Not exactly a fortune, Mrs Pennykettle."

"He's priceless to us," said Liz.

Sergeant Beale stepped forward with a digital camera. "Do you mind if I take a snapshot of one, just in case we collar this bloke?"

Without waiting for permission, Sergeant Beale trained his camera back and forth on Gruffen. There was a flash. The sergeant checked the image – and frowned. "That's odd," he said. "I could have sworn it wasn't smiling before I took the shot."

His superior officer sighed. "Let's get on with the questioning, shall we, Beale? Have any of you seen anything suspicious lately? Any strange people lurking near the house?"

Lucy thought for a moment, then her face suddenly lit up. "*We* haven't," she said, "but the d—"

"Dog at number 30 has been barking," said Liz, clamping her hand over Lucy's mouth. "Perhaps, they've noticed something?"

Inspector Bumble raised his chin, in the manner of a man who suspected that a secret was being kept from him. He threw a lop-sided glance at Lucy.

Teeth gritted, she offered him a silent grin.

"Can you give us a rough idea of

what time the break-in took place?" asked Beale, licking the tip of his pencil as he waited.

Liz glanced sideways at Gauge. In a flash, the timing dragon moved his arms to indicate 9:15 on the clock.

"Quarter past nine?" she said, as if it were a guess.

Sergeant Beale jotted it down. "And was anything else taken?"

"No," Liz said, "just a dragon. But the robber did leave something behind…"

From her pinafore pocket, she produced a bag of sweets.

"Ah, barley sugars," said Henry, his eyes lighting up. "My favourites. Very kind, Mrs P." He reached forward to take one.

Liz slapped his wrist. "These are evidence, Henry."

"*Sweets?*" said Lucy.

Sergeant Beale nodded. "He sometimes leaves pear drops or sherbet lemons."

Lucy wrinkled her nose. "Why would a robber leave sweets?"

Inspector Bumble put a finger underneath his hat. He pushed it back slightly, exposing a line of wrinkles on his forehead. "An excellent question, Miss. When we arrest him, and interrogate him, I'll let you know." And he unwrapped a barley sugar and popped it into his mouth. He turned to Liz. "I have to tell you that the chances of recovering your dragon are slim."

"I bet you we find him," Lucy said, pitching forward.

Inspector Bumble hummed, not unlike a bee. "Here's my card," he said, bending down to her. (The card was crumpled and smelled of mints.) "If you see anything odd, you give me a call."

"Might," said Lucy, with a sullen sniff.

The Inspector wagged a finger at her. He placed his hands in the small of his back and sipped his breath as he straightened himself up.

Henry picked up a frying pan. "We'll be ready for him if he comes back."

Inspector Bumble gave Henry a disapproving frown. "If I were you, I'd use that for cooking, sir. Unless you want to end up in the police station yourself." He tipped his trilby hat towards Liz. "Thank you. We'll let ourselves out."

And then he and his sergeant were gone.

"You too," Liz said to Henry Bacon. She took back her pan and pointed to the garden like a referee sending a footballer off the field.

Henry gestured to the broken glass. "Unfinished business, Mrs P. I'll pop round later. Fix this in a jiff. Probably find an old piece of glass in a skip. Not worth paying for new."

"No you won't," Liz said, pushing him out. "We'll get a professional glazier in. And take this with you." She pressed the empty flour bag into his hand. It gave out one last feeble puff.

"But—?"

"Go, Henry." She closed the door in his face before he could argue.

As Mr Bacon trooped solemnly away, Liz reached up to a shelf, grabbed a telephone directory and plonked it down with a dusty *thwap* on the worktop. Gruffen watched in fascination as she thumbed its yellow pages for entries beginning with the letter 'G' for glaziers.

"Mum, wait," Lucy said. She put her hand on the book, preventing her mum from turning the pages. "The dragons must know what the robber looked like." She glanced at all three in turn. Gauge nodded and spoke in dragontongue to her. "See? Gauge says he was old and

38

fat, in a black woolly hat. If we tell the police, they'll catch him right away."

Liz grabbed Lucy's hand and moved it onto the worktop. "And how are we going to explain *that* at a trial?" Mimicking a judge's deep voice, she said, "How did you come by this description of the accused, Miss Pennykettle?" Then she mimicked Lucy's reedy voice. "Oh, my dragon told me, m'lud."

Lucy folded her arms and tutted in defeat.

"Now, glaziers," said Liz. "This one should do." She pressed her finger to an advert in the book. "Mr R. Badfellow. Twenty-four hour glass repair service. Local, too."

She picked up the telephone and dialled a number. "Hello, Mr Badfellow? Yes. I wondered if you could replace a couple of panes of glass in my back door for me? No, we had a break in last night. Nothing much stolen, thankfully."

Lucy snorted heavily at that.

"The name is Pennykettle. We're at 42 Wayward Crescent. Hello? Did you catch that? You sounded quite surprised. 42, yes. Thank you. Thank you very much." She put the phone down. "He'll be round in half an hour. At least we won't have a gale blowing through the house tonight."

"We should tell the police what the robber looks like," Lucy said glumly, falling back with a foot raised flat against the fridge. It rocked a little, making the listening dragon hurr. "We need to get our dragon back."

Just then, the letterbox rattled. Lucy looked up the hall in time to see two letters fall onto the mat. As they did, an idea popped into her head. Letters. She opened her hand and looked at Inspector Bumble's card. There was an address on it. Maybe…? "I don't have to be here when the gazer comes, do I?"

"It's glazier," said Liz. "No, you don't."

Lucy grinned. "OK. I'm going to my room now." And calling Gauge and Gruffen to follow, she hurried upstairs.

Chapter Four

Meanwhile, in a small untidy house on a large untidy estate, Mr R. Badfellow, glazier by trade, was tapping his chin and looking thoughtfully at the telephone. "Well, this is a very rum do," he said. "A very rum do indeed." His gaze travelled to the canvas bag of tools on the floor, particularly at the flashlight which he sometimes used for his evening work. "Risky," he said. "Very irregular. Not in the rules of robbing at all." He put his hands into his threadbare pockets. "Could be a trap. Could be rozzers afoot." He hummed and picked up a cracked old mug, took a swig of stale tea and scratched his bottom. Then he walked across the room, limping slightly from an ancient injury with a garden fence (one that he cared not to think about) and wagged a finger at the little green dragon he had locked into a bird cage he'd nicked from a house in Upper Scrubbley one time. Looking into its strangely violet eyes he said, "In this bizness, one 'as to be careful crafty."

Hrrr, went the dragon, pricking its ears. Faster than the human eye could see, it put a paw through the bars of the cage and grabbed the end of the man's finger.

Mr R. Badfellow smiled. The gaps in his teeth were plugged by fish. Tuna, ice cream, the occasional red apple and boiled eggs with soldiers was all he ever ate. "You're a very strange trinket, you are," he said. "Worth every barley sugar in that bag." He glanced sideways at a pair of bowed wooden shelves, which were straining under the weight of two or three dozen sweet shop jars, all containing different kinds of sweets. "And maybe worth a lot more than sweets," he muttered as his eyes turned misty and he glanced at a picture of a young boy with a teddy bear, hanging on the wall. He returned his gaze to the cage. "I would like to find out more about you. So I will fix this lady's glass. I will return to the scene of my robbing. I will scrutinize. I'll sniff. My eye will peruse. My ears will wiggle. Then we'll decide what's what, little grabber."

Hrrr! went the dragon, making the cage rattle.

Mr Badfellow smiled. "Grabber. I like that. A good name for a robber's mate, that is." With a tug (for the dragon was surprisingly strong) Mr Badfellow freed his finger. "You stay in your cage and be good, you hear? Old Ron, he's got a little call to make…"

Chapter Five

By the time he'd turned up at Wayward Crescent, Mr Badfellow had donned a disguise. No black boots or jacket or hat. For his glazing work he always wore denim bib overalls, heavily smeared with dobs of putty, over a T-shirt turning yellow underneath the arms. He had also pulled on a filthy white cap, with a peak so beaky that it curved like a sunshade over and around his thick-rimmed glasses. Just for good measure, a false moustache now rode above his top lip. No one, not even the dragons of Wayward Crescent, would have recognised him as Ron the robber.

On arrival, Liz invited him from the front step down the side of the house. She met him again at the kitchen door.

"Tsk tsk," he said, as he inspected the damage. "That's the work of a robber for sure. There are some scoundrels about and no mistake."

"Yes," Liz agreed. "Would you

like a cup of tea?"

"Very kind," Mr Badfellow said, using the politest voice he could. "Two bags and four sugars, with just a drop of milk, so it looks like treacle."

"Erm, right," said Liz. She flipped open the lid of the kettle and filled it.

Mr Badfellow took a tape measure from his overalls and proceeded to size up the broken glass. "So, did the rogue take off with much?"

"Only one thing. A dragon. I make them."

"You *make* them?"

"Yes. You sound surprised."

Very bad, thought Ron. *Very bad indeed. A slip in the voice. A sign of guilt.* "Just shock," he said, coughing into his fist. "It's always the sentimental trinkets that go."

Liz nodded and plugged in the kettle.

At that moment, Mr Badfellow

glanced across the kitchen and caught sight of the listening dragon on the fridge. "Is that one of them there?"

"Yes," said Liz.

"My, it's got wondrous big ears, has it not?"

"All the better for listening with."

"I see," said Ron. "It listens, does it?"

"Only if you speak its language," said Liz. She smiled.

Mr Ron Badfellow, the robber, smiled back. *Very odd,* he thought. *Very strange indeed. Here's me fibbing through my fishy teeth. But what about this lady? Could she be fibbing too? Teasing, perhaps? About her dragons?*

"The robber left us some sweets. Would you like one?" said Liz.

Mr Badfellow gulped. A band of sweat was building up beneath his cap, making his deepest wrinkles itch. "No, thank you, missus, not good for the teeth."

Liz had one anyway. She rather liked sweets.

Against his better judgement, Ron found himself asking, "What kind of a robber would leave you a gift?"

"I don't think he's a proper robber," said Liz.

"You don't?" Mr Badfellow gulped again.

"No. I think he's doing it because he's unhappy."

"I see," said Ron, though he didn't

much really – his false glasses were beginning to steam up. *This lady*, he was thinking. *Most odd indeed. Nail, poink! upon the head she had hit. He was unhappy. But how could he say? He couldn't. The truth must never come out.*

"Will the job take long?"

Ron stared at the glass. "Half an hour. Good as new."

"Wonderful," Liz said, moving out of the kitchen. "Give me a shout when you're done."

She put a barley sugar into her mouth and was gone.

And so Ron the robber continued his work and was true to his word about the timing. After thirty minutes the glass was repaired. He called Liz back.

She inspected the door. "Smashing – sorry, no pun intended. How much do I owe you?"

"Twenty pounds should clear it. Do you mind if I use your facilities?"

"Facilities? Oh, you mean the bathroom? Yes, of course. It's the room facing the top of the stairs."

"Much obliged," said Ron. Here was his chance. The moment to investigate further had come. Upstairs he went, treading softly, creaking the same steps he'd creaked the night before.

As he reached the landing, the first thing he noticed was a sign on the door to his left. It was hand-painted, gold and green, with bright orange flames leaping up

around the lettering. DRAGONS'
DEN. It was the room where he'd
found the little grabber at home.
The perfect place to start his
snooping. But as he was reaching out
to turn the handle he heard a girl's
voice in the room next door. He
paused with a start.

"OK, how does this sound?" she
was saying.

Ron crept along the landing and
peered through the crack between
the door and the frame. The girl was
sitting cross-legged on her bed,
reading a letter to two more dragons.

"Dear police, this is a nominuss tip-off. I know who did the robbing in Wayward Crescent. He is quite old and dumpy. He wears a black woolly hat and jacket and boots. He speaks in a growly voice like a bear. And he smells of fish. Please catch him quickly. A friend." She picked up a pen. "Shall I put a kiss on it?"

Mr Ron Badfellow turned away. *Not good*, he thought. *Not good at all. Clocked by dragons. Voice overheard. Something must be done. Action taken.*

Hearing Lucy moving, he went to the bathroom and quickly flushed the toilet. Then he hurried downstairs to the kitchen, where Liz handed him twenty pounds.

"Thank you," said Ron. He

stuffed the money into his overalls pocket, then turned and stared at the listening dragon. *So, this one could hear voices, could it?* "Very pretty," said Ron. "A rare bauble indeed. Do you mind if I...?" He reached out a hand.

"Not at all," Liz said. "Just be careful with its ears."

"As a mouse," said Ron, meaning he'd be gentle, which indeed he was. And clever, too. For there was a small glob of putty concealed between his fingers. Using all the deftness he would use with glass, he rubbed his thumbs deep into the petal-like ears, then smiled and put the listener back onto the fridge. There, no one would talk to this dragon in a hurry and ask it questions about any robber.

"You didn't finish your tea," said Liz. "Would you like a fresh one before you go?"

"No, thank you," said Ron, picking up the mug. "I like it cold, missus." He was about to take a slurp when Lucy scooted into the kitchen.

"Oh, hello," she said to Ron.

He coughed, making his false moustache jiggle.

Lucy sniffed the air for a moment.

"Are we having fish tonight?" She frowned at Ron. Suspiciously, he thought. He hastily put the mug to his mouth and began to swig the remainder of the tea.

Lucy shrugged and turned to her mum. "Can I have a stamp, please? First class. Now."

"What's so important that it needs a first class stamp?"

Mr Ron Badfellow knew the answer, but he wasn't going to hang around and hear it said. He drank the last of the tea and even rinsed the mug in the sink for good measure. "I'll be off, then," he said and strolled out without looking at either Liz or Lucy again.

But he'd only gone a few yards

when he heard Lucy squeal. "Agh! Mum! There's an earwig in the sink!"

"Don't be silly," said her mother. "Show me. Where?"

"I flushed it away," Ron heard Lucy say.

Earwig? He felt the top of his lip. Strewth! There was no moustache! It must have come off in the tea!

And the girl had seen it and thought it was a wriggler! Heart pounding, he walked on as fast as his limp would allow. He'd had a lucky escape. A lucky escape indeed! He took off his glasses and wiped his brow. Then he threw his bag into the back of his van and roared away up Wayward Crescent.

Chapter Six

Now, while all this was taking place, the new dragon had not been idle. Since the moment that Ron had named him Grabber, some strange ideas had been running through his mind. For a start, he'd had a very strong urge to break out of his cage.

It was a pleasant cage with good views all around the room, but there was something about being behind bars which troubled him. It troubled him so much that shortly after Ron had left the house, Grabber had gripped two bars in his paws and tried to pull them wide enough apart so that he might slip through and fly free...

...but the bars were too strong and he sank back with an exhausted *hrrr*.

Then he had the peculiar idea that he might angle the scales on his tail in such a way that he might use them to saw through the bars...

...but that just hurt his tail.

Then his violet eyes settled on the

small brass lock on the cage door. His ears pricked as his mind began to understand its workings. How he could do this, who could say? But somehow he knew what was needed to unlock it. Quickly, he flipped his tail through the bars. Then, curving the tip right round so that his very last scale (which dragons call their isoscele) was pointing at the lock, he pushed his tail into the keyhole and twisted it. The lock gave a satisfying click. The bolt snapped back and the door clicked open.

And Grabber was out!

Ron's house was no palace, it has to be said. His front room was frankly a dreadful mess. Unwashed plates were slid under chairs. Apple cores were wedged down the sides of the sofa. The carpet smelled of milk gone sour. The nets at the windows were so thick with grime that they shut out three-quarters of the morning sun. And, as if things weren't shabby enough, strung from wall to wall was a loopy washing line, upon which several pairs of socks and some underpants were drying. A pair of dirty boots were up there too, hanging from their knotted laces.

Shocking.

As for possessions, Ron had next to none. Apart from a small TV in the corner (with a wonky coat hanger for an aerial) and a tea-stained radio and a vase of flowers (Ron did like a nice spray of lilies) there were very few objects of interest or value. But on the mantelpiece above a gas fire with charred and broken radiants, Grabber found a small drawstring bag. It was full of matches. He hurred on one. To his delight the match set aflame. Yet it was the bag, not the matches, that intrigued him the most. So much so, that after a few seconds some irresistible urge made him tip the matches out and sling the bag across his shoulder, where it seemed to lie,

quite naturally, as if his body had been made for it. He tapped his foot and looked around, using his eyes like flashlights in the gloom. He saw a spinning top Ron had recently stolen, flew to it and set it in motion. In fact he rode it round the floor for several minutes and nearly turned his brains to soup in the process! When at last he grew tired and fluttered off, he landed groggily on a sideboard where he found a small, padlocked treasure chest. With a rush of excitement he dibbled the lock and flipped the clasp. There were some shiny pebbles inside. He took out a purple one and hurred on it gently. Its glassy centre twinkled like a star. Grabber wrinkled his snout. A strange word, 'SWAG', came into his mind. He popped the pebble into his bag and drew the string. It seemed the most natural thing to do.

Then, almost by chance, his eye was taken by the picture on the wall of a little boy and an old teddy bear. The same one Ron had stared at earlier. Grabber tilted his head this way and that. He grizzled his teeth. He tapped his foot. He swished his tail. Why a photo of a teddy should catch his imagination he couldn't say. Was it the soulful look in the teddy's eyes? Or the innocence in the boy's, perhaps? Or was it the grubby thumb prints on one corner of the frame that intrigued him? Mmm…

Spreading his wings, he quickly flew to it and hovered just in front of the well-thumbed corner. Instinct encouraged him to touch the frame. The picture tilted and swung to one side, as if it had done this many times before. Grabber pushed harder.

So hard that the picture jostled off its nail and slid to the floor. And lo and behold, hidden in the wall behind it was a safe.

Now, Grabber had no idea what a safe was. To him it was just another thing to play with. He squeezed its handle. Nothing happened. He hurred on the handle. Still nothing happened. So he focused his attention on the large grey knob in the centre of the safe. When he grabbed it with his paws and turned it either way he thought he could hear a mechanism clicking. He pressed one ear to the metal and listened. Click, click, clickety-clonk…

…kerdumph.

Something had sprung. Another bolt, perhaps? Grabber tried the handle again. Charisma! This time the door swung open.

Inside the safe was a heap of jewellery: rings and bracelets and fine silver necklaces. But on top of the heap was something rather odd. A lollipop. A round one, wrapped in shiny paper, on the end of a short white stick.

Grabber's eyes doubled to twice their size.

SWAG!

Just at that moment, a door banged elsewhere in the house. With a flutter of panic, Grabber flew away, forgetting to close the safe or put back the picture or cover his robbing trail at all. He was so anxious not to be caught that he headed straight back towards his cage. But in his haste and his youthful inexperience at flying, he clipped the lampshade with his wing. Down, down, down he spiralled, until he fell, of all places, into one of Ron's socks!

When Ron came in, imagine his surprise to see his wall safe nearly burgled, his bird cage open and the little dragon that should have been inside it upside down with his head poking out of the toes of a sock.

The game was up for Grabber. No matter how hard he wriggled, he couldn't break free. When Ron unpegged the sock, Grabber didn't try to struggle. He simply blushed (dark green) and gave a sad little *hrrr*.

His first foray into robbing had been a disaster.

It was a fair cop.

Chapter Seven

Thankfully, Ron wasn't angry. He merely chortled heartily and sat the sock (and its contents) upright on his palm. "Well, well, little Grabber. What games 'ave *you* been up to?"

Grabber gave out a bashful *hrrr*.

Ron's gaze travelled sideways to

the safe. "You've discovered my haul and my lollipop, I see. There's a story about that lolly. Shall I tell you?"

Grabber *hrrred* again and wiggled his ears. Ron's words were little more than grunts to him. But the tone of them was pleasant and made him feel cared for. Mind you, when Ron reached into his canvas bag and flashed a pair of scissors in front of Grabber's snout, the little dragon did begin to wobble in alarm.

Ron calmed him with a soothing shush. The scissors clicked and snipped, but only to cut holes in the sock for Grabber's arms and legs and wings and tail.

Strangely, Ron left the body of the sock in place, so that it looked like

Grabber was wearing a jumper. A black and white hooped jumper. This made Ron chuckle even more.

"You look a proper rascal now," he said.

Grabber curved an ear.

Ron carried him across to an old battered sideboard, opened a drawer and took out an envelope. He shook some photographs out of it. And there was one of Ron, in a black and white hooped jumper, wearing a robber's mask!

Grabber sat back in surprise.

"I have been a bad fellow," Ron Badfellow said. "I've lived up to my name and no mistake. I began my robbing ways all because of that lollipop."

Grabber tilted his head. He could not understand Ron's words, but Pennykettle dragons don't have to speak a language to recognize loss or heartache or despair. In a blink, Grabber fluttered up to sit on Ron's shoulder. Ron was unsurprised. By now he had accepted there was something rather magical about his new friend. So he simply went about his business, tidying the room and muttering some more about the story of the lollipop.

He picked up the picture of the teddy bear and boy. "This is me with Humphrey,"  he said. "The best Christmas present I ever had." He ran his fingers along the bear's snout, brushing aside a streak of dust. "One night, a villain broke into our house and snatched him from the foot of my bed. I was fast a-zuzzing. So were Ma and Pa. The robber left this lollipop where Humphrey had been sitting." He reached into the safe and took out the sweet. "I suppose he thought it was a kindness, Grabber. But it broke my heart. I've been looking for that villain – and my teddy – ever since."

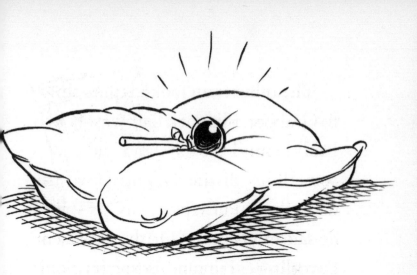

He closed the safe and put the picture on its hook. "I thought it was a hopeless mission, I did. But a month or two ago, I had a stroke of luck." He turned to the TV and slid in a video, then pointed a remote control at the screen.

Grabber did a double take. There on the screen was Humphrey the teddy bear. He was sitting on a table between two men. One of them was grey-haired and elderly and kind.

The other man looked quite shifty to Grabber. His dark hair was slicked back behind his ears and there was something distinctly untrustworthy about him. Perhaps it was his spiky-ended moustache? Or the small and sparkling earring he wore? His teeth were far too shiny as well. Grabber took an instant dislike to him.

Ron said, "This is a show I watch every week. People bring their trinkets to be valued. Oh, yes. I nearly spilled a whole mug of tea, I did, when I saw my Humphrey on the show. He's become an antique. Worth a pretty penny. Five thousand smackers to be precise." He paused the screen on a close-up of the shiny-toothed man. "This is the rogue who is holding him hostage. His name is Douglas Crumbe. He has made a fortune from selling biscuits. How he came to have Humphrey, I do not know. I have discovered that this smarmy-looking fellow lives in a house on Cosytoes Lane, a very posh part of Scrubbley. I don't think he would ever give

Humphrey back, but he might be persuaded to sell him, Grabber. All those pretty things in the safe will soon add up to five thousand pounds. It's not right to take things from the good people of Scrubbley to pay for my bear, but I am a desperate man." Ron twiddled the lollipop in his fingers. "Just a few more houses. Just a few more robbings. Then I should have enough. Then you and I will pay Mr Crumbe a visit…"

Chapter Eight

Meanwhile, back in Wayward Crescent, Liz was beginning to suspect that something wasn't right. For the last two days, since the visit of the policemen, the kitchen had been remarkably quiet. At first, she couldn't decide what was wrong.

When she looked around the room, everything was in its proper place. The refrigerator was humming. The tap dripped as it sometimes did. And from the garden came the lively chatter of birds. And yet…

She glanced at the listening dragon on the fridge.

"Do *you* think it's quiet?" she asked.

The listener, seeing her lips move, smiled.

Liz narrowed her eyes and squinted at it. "Are you all right? Did you hear what I said?"

The listener blew a bemused little smoke ring.

Liz clicked her tongue. She turned to Gauge, who was sitting on the worktop, and said something quietly to him in dragontongue.

Seconds later, Gauge had fluttered (unseen) to the back of the fridge top. He crept up behind the listener and hurred.

The listener barely twitched its ears.

Liz gave a thoughtful hum.

Suddenly, the kitchen door opened and Henry Bacon came in once more. "Can't stop," he said.

"Oh, shame," Liz muttered, only *slightly* clenching her teeth.

Henry slapped a drawing in front of her. It was a complicated sketch of wires and pulleys, built around a door frame. Above the door was some kind of hooter and a frying pan.

"Bacon's patent intruder defence system," he beamed. "Any unwanted persons stepping on my welcome mat will get a hoot in their ear hole and a lump on their bonce from my frying pan. Want me to set it up for you, Mrs P?"

"No, I do not," Liz said huffily, just as the doorbell rang.

Lucy pounded downstairs to answer it. A moment or two later she came down the hall followed by Inspector Bumble and Sergeant Beale. "Mum, it's *the police* again."

"I'm off," said Henry. He was gone in a flash.

Liz met the Inspector's gaze.

"Mrs Pennykettle, I'll come straight to the point," he said. "I believe you know who broke into your house."

He flapped a piece of paper. It was Lucy's note.

Lucy turned on her heels and tried to escape. But Inspector Bumble clamped her shoulder and turned her round, red-faced, to her mother.

"We received a tip-off," said Beale.

"Oh, really?" said Liz. She didn't seem at all surprised. "Was it signed 'love from Lucy' by any chance?"

"I never!" cried Lucy. She turned furiously to the Inspector. "How did you know it was from me?"

"Call it a calculated guess," he replied. He pointed to the top of the note, which carried Liz's business logo: Pennykettle Pots and Crafts. "Next time you send an anonymous message, it would be wise not to put your address on it, *Miss*."

"Oh," said Lucy, looking a bit embarrassed.

"All right, you can let her off," said Liz. "I think I do know who your robber is."

"Oh yes?" said Beale. He reached for his notebook.

Liz walked across the kitchen and reached for the listener. She quickly examined its ears and said, "His name is Ronald Badfellow. He came to mend the glass in our door."

Sergeant Beale scribbled this down.

Inspector Bumble pushed back his coat and put his hands firmly onto his hips. "And why would you think the robber is him?"

"Because he's plugged the ears of my listening dragon with putty."

"What?" gasped Lucy.

"Listening dragon?" Inspector Bumble said in a voice which suggested Liz was quite barmy.

"Yes. I think Mr Badfellow might have guessed that my dragons are real."

"Mum?" hissed Lucy. "What are you playing at?"

Liz smiled and dug a glob of putty out of the listener's ear. It responded by lifting its wing and kicking at the shell of its ear like a cat. "Would you like a cup of tea?" she asked the policemen.

Lucy glanced up. The eyes of both men were almost spinning. Liz had used her magic on them. They sat down and mumbled, "Yes."

Liz cleared out the listener's other

ear. "Good. Lucy, put the kettle on, please. I think we'll all have a quiet drink – and then we'll go and pay Mr Badfellow a visit…"

Chapter Nine

Of course, it was not at all difficult for the two policemen to quickly find Ronald Badfellow's address (especially when they'd been ordered to do so with a little more 'magic' from Liz). But by the time they had reached the small house on the estate, Ron the robber and his tiny partner in crime were already out on the prowl.

That night, Ron drove his van down Cosytoes Lane, where Mr Douglas Crumbe had his house. It was called Custard Cream Towers, a tribute to Mr Crumbe's success in the biscuit trade.

Ron pulled up outside a pair of gigantic solid gates. "Look, Grabber. Mr Crumbe's home. A fortress, it is, to be sure."

Grabber, who was sitting on top of the dashboard, gave a questioning *hrrr* and swished his tail.

Ron pointed at the gates. "Humphrey. Through there."

Grabber dibbled his toes.

Hrrrmphrey. Gradually, he was beginning to learn what Ron's grunts meant. He glanced at the gates. The teddy? That way?

"No good," said Ron, guessing his intention. "I have thought many times about pilfering the place. But this is too grand for petty scoundrels like us. A sparrow could not take a crust of bread from these lawns without setting off a dozen alarms."

Grabber frowned thoughtfully. When he did this, something peculiar happened. The ridges round his eyes turned from dark green to black, until it looked as if he was wearing his own robber's mask. He glanced down. There were some buttons on the door of the van. His dragon instincts told him that one of them, if pushed, would open the window. Within seconds, he'd done it and was gone.

When Ron caught up with him, Grabber was hovering in front of a number pad attached to the wall at the side of the gates.

Ron shook his head. "To make the gates open, one 'as to press the numbers in the right order, Grabber. But it's impossible. There are more combinations than sweets in my jars." He pressed four numbers, then a key marked 'OPEN'. A red light beeped, but the gates remained closed.

Grabber tried a few buttons himself. Nothing happened. He twitched his snout and tried a few more. Still nothing.

"See," said Ron. "It would take…"

He was about to say 'for ever'. But before he could complete his sentence, Grabber's claws were moving so fast over the numbers that his paws were just a blur. Suddenly, there was a click and the grinding noise of motors.

"Stone the crows!" Ron gasped. The gates were sliding apart. Grabber had cracked the lock in under three seconds!

Hrrr! went the dragon, and flew inside.

"Wait!" Ron cried, as his small green companion in his hooped sock vest suddenly became a dot in the distance. Ron sipped his breath. The rush of cold air found the gaps in his teeth, putting all his ageing nerves on edge. This was a most irregular caper. Risky. Unplanned. Sure to end badly. But a partner was a partner. And partners had a saying:

all for one and both…for prison, at this rate. He locked the van and went in pursuit.

Custard Cream Towers was nothing like its name. The walls were as brown as a Bourbon biscuit. And as Ron tiptoed silently between the conifer bushes that grew all along the S-shaped drive, he saw that the house was only two storeys high, not like a tower at all.

Suddenly, an exterior light flashed on, illuminating a sturdy door. Ron crouched behind an ornamental statue. He could see Grabber hovering in front of the door, as if he was caught in a spaceship's tractor beam.

"Come away," Ron hissed. "You'll never get in." This was a fair assessment. Any gentleman of the night would not have stood a chance of cracking the security. Even from a distance Ron could see that the door was protected by a moving video camera, at least three locks, and a burglar alarm that was winking, red and green, above the door.

But this was nothing to a *dragon* of the night. Grabber switched his swag bag to his opposite shoulder, fluttered down to the level of the letterbox, lifted the flap, had a peek inside and flew straight through!

Moments later the video camera had stopped moving, the burglar alarm had ceased to blink and the door had given three soft clunks. Ron couldn't believe it. Grabber had disabled the security system.

They were in!

Chapter Ten

The house had a cold, unpleasant kind of feel. There was nothing on the walls. No carpets on the floors. Not even a lampshade covering the light bulbs.

Odd, thought Ron. *Very odd indeed. Here's this Douglas Crumbe, making millions from biscuits. Yet his house is as plain as an old cream cracker.* Where were all the trinkets? Family portraits? Ornaments? Where was Humphrey, come to that?

Ron didn't have long to wait for an answer. Suddenly, a light went on in a room above the stairs. Ron pressed himself into the shadows and waited. There was no sound, except for a tiny voice going *hrrr*!

It was a *hrrr* of surprise, strong enough to draw Ron out of hiding. He crept up to the room and peered inside. Lumme lawks! It was FULL of teddies.

They were in heaps and bundles, and bundles upon heaps. All shapes. All sizes. Mostly brown. Mostly old.

A tingle of excitement rushed through Ron's bones. All his years of searching, all his years of loss, were about to end. Humphrey *had* to be here. He could almost sense the old bear's sorrowful growling, the way he always did if you tipped him up.

103

But then Ron took a nervous gulp. For there were so many bears cast about this room, so many Humphrey look-alikes, that it might take an hour or two to find his bear among them. And robbers rarely had an hour or two. Smash, grab, go. That was how it was. Get in fast. Get out even faster. But not in this case. Time must be taken. Humphrey *must* be found. So Ron put aside his canvas bag and began to sift the teddies. He'd been at it for only seconds when he heard a footfall by the door.

He turned in shock, with an armful of bears. There was Douglas Crumbe, smoking a cigar.

"Well, well," said Crumbe. "What have we here?"

"I don't want no trouble," said Ron.

"It's a little bit late for that," said Crumbe. He gave a sickly, short-lived smile. "I won't ask how you broke through my considerable security; you're obviously a very talented crook. But I am intrigued to know what you want with my bears."

 "You stole one!" cried Ron. "From me, from my bed, when I was just a nipper! He's called Humphrey!"

Mr Douglas Crumbe coughed with smoke and laughter. "Forgive me, but you are...sixty, perhaps? And I am in the peak of life, as you can see. I would not have been born when you were a boy."

"Then your father," said Ron. "Or someone you knew. Where did you get these handsome bears?"

"Handsome?" Douglas Crumbe stroked his moustache. "I assure you, sir, there are few things in life more handsome than me!"

His face disappeared behind a cloud of bluish smoke. By the time it was visible again, there was a glint of wickedness in  his eyes. "Where I got them from is no business of yours. However, you're welcome to take any you choose."

"Really?" said Ron, slightly taken aback. Why would this schmoozy rogue say that?

"Be my guest," said Crumbe. "You'll be doing me a favour. When the police arrive to investigate the fire, I will describe you to them. They will, of course, believe me when I say you caused the blaze."

"Fire?" asked Ron with a gulp.

Douglas Crumbe showed his teeth. "These ridiculous bags of fluff and wool that my sentimental father left me in his will are an embarrassment. It would take far too long to sell them. I really can't be bothered. I need money fast. My biscuit empire is crumbling. So I'm going to burn down this house and claim the insurance. These teddies will make perfect kindling, don't you think? Best of all, by turning them to ash I can claim their worth too. It's the perfect crime. Goodbye, robber. Goodbye, bears." He lifted the lit cigar into the air.

"No!" cried Ron.

But Douglas Crumbe merely

smiled and flicked his cigar towards the bears.

The situation looked hopeless. But suddenly, there was a flash of movement and the cigar was caught in mid-air – by a dragon!

"What the blazes?" cried Crumbe, even though there were no blazes. For Grabber had not only caught the cigar, he had swallowed the heat of the thing and doused it. He spat the foul-tasting stick onto the floor.

"Come 'ere, you!" Ron the robber said, and he launched himself, fists flying, at Crumbe.

Biff. Bash. Clobber. Clout. The punches flew this way and that. Ron, being older and slower than his rival, took the last one hard in the tummy. Oof. He staggered backwards and splashed into the bears.

Douglas Crumbe wiped a trickle of blood from his mouth. He notched his tie straight and slicked his hair. He grimaced at his beaten foe.

"Fool," he sneered, and took out another cigar. But before he could light it, Grabber was there, right in front of his face.

"You again?" said Crumbe.

Grabber hurred and reached into his swag bag for something.

"A lollipop?" laughed Crumbe.

Hrrr, went Grabber, and struck it soundly on the horrid man's forehead, right between his shifty eyes.

Douglas Crumbe softened like a digestive biscuit dunked into a cup of very hot tea.

Then, suddenly, a siren was sounding outside on the drive and the shadow of a blue light was flashing at the window.

"The rozzers!" cried Ron, trying to struggle to his feet. "We're cooked! Run f'rit, Grabber!"

Too late. Sergeant Beale and Inspector Bumble were already in the room, quickly followed by Liz and Lucy.

"Ronald Badfellow," Inspector Bumble said. "I'm arresting you on multiple counts of robbing."

Sergeant Beale snapped a pair of handcuffs onto Ron.

"I only did it for the bear!" he cried.

The two policemen bundled him downstairs.

"And where do you think you're going?" Liz said in dragontongue to the fleeing Grabber. One look from her violet eyes was enough to mesmerise him, mid-flight.

"Cor," said Lucy as he fell into her hands. "He really *looks* like a robber, Mum."

"Hmm," went Liz. "Well, it's nothing to be proud of. That vest is coming off and *he* is coming home with us…"

Epilogue

As it happened, Grabber's vest stayed on. Liz finally came around to Lucy's suggestion that the hooped sock actually suited him. Even so, she warned, he would need to stay in Guinevere's care for a while and be taught that robbing, even for a 'good' cause, was bad.

"It wasn't *his* fault, though," Lucy said. "If Ron hadn't named him Grabber he wouldn't be like this. Will we have to rename him?"

"No," said Liz. "But we will have to re-educate him. Then, in time, he can go back to Ron."

Lucy's mouth fell open.

"I think that's where he'd be happiest, don't you?" Liz smiled at the young dragon, who was sitting on the kitchen table with Gruffen and Gauge.

"What will happen to Ron?" asked Lucy. "Will he have to go to prison?"

"He's appearing in court today,"

said Liz, just as the doorbell rang. "That might be the police now. Inspector Bumble said he'd call round and give us any news."

Sure enough, when Lucy opened the door, there were the two figures of Bumble and Beale. She took them through to the kitchen, where Liz offered them some cake and a cup of tea.

"So," she said. "What happened to Ron?"

"Wrist slapped," the Inspector said.

"No prison sentence, but the judge has given him six months' community service."

"What does that mean?" asked Lucy.

"Do you know that old factory beside Scrubbley Common?" said Sergeant Beale.

"The one with all its windows smashed?" said Lucy.

Beale nodded. "Mr Badfellow has to glaze them all."

"Very fitting," said Liz. "What about Douglas Crumbe?"

Inspector Bumble swallowed a mouthful of cake. "We've charged him with attempted fraud. He'll go to prison. He's the real crook."

"And what's going to happen to the

bears?" said Lucy. She'd been dying to ask this from the word go.

Annoyingly, she had to wait another ten seconds while the Inspector washed his cake down with a swig of tea. "The bears are a genuine collection," he said. "They were all purchased by Alaistair Crumbe, Douglas Crumbe's father, and passed on to his very ungrateful son. Some of them are worth a mint. Nice payday for that rascal if they had gone up in smoke."

"Yes, but where's *Humphrey?*" Lucy said with a huff.

"Ronald Badfellow has identified a bear he claims belongs to him," said Sergeant Beale.

"Will he get him back?" asked Liz.

The two policemen looked at one another. Sergeant Beale took out his notes and said, "Alaistair Crumbe kept records of his purchases. We're investigating the man he bought Humphrey from. The man has a criminal record. If he confesses to stealing Humphrey, he'll be returned to Ronald Badfellow."

"Yes!" said Lucy, tightening her fists.

"By the way," the Inspector said, reaching into his pocket for a photograph. "You had a dragon stolen, did you not?" He glanced around, but Grabber had flown across to the worktop and was hiding behind Sergeant Beale, fearing he might be arrested.

"Did it look anything like this?" He put the photo down.

Lucy caught her breath. The picture was of Grabber, hovering in a beam of light.

"It was taken by a video camera at Crumbe's house."

"Goodness, how odd," said Liz. "Well, even if it was one of ours we'd never identify it, would we? It's in disguise!"

Sergeant Beale coughed. "Well, perhaps I could take a few details of what your stolen dragon looked like anyway, Mrs Pennykettle?" He reached into his jacket for his pencil, but it wasn't there. "Oh," he said, patting his pockets. "I seem to have mislaid my pencil."

"Never mind," said Inspector Bumble. "Something tells me we won't find this dragon. Would I be right, Mrs Pennykettle?" He smiled thinly at Liz. She smiled broadly back. The inspector tipped his hat. "Good day, madam. Thank you for the tea."

"Good day," said Liz.

Lucy escorted the policemen to the door.

When she came back into the kitchen, Liz was frowning hard at Grabber. "Open your bag," Liz said to him.

Hrrr? went Grabber, trying to sound innocent.

"Open it," Liz said. Her green eyes flashed.

Grabber gulped and spilled the contents of the bag onto the table.

"Hey, that's one of my hair clips!" cried Lucy. "And my favourite bookmark! And the pebble from my room! He's pinched them!"

"And Sergeant Beale's pencil, by the look of it," Liz said, as a stubby one dropped at Grabber's feet.

Grabber gulped apologetically and picked it up. As he did so, Liz gave a little start.

"What's the matter?" asked Lucy.

Liz covered her heart. "Oh, the strangest feeling," she said.

"A dragon with a pencil."

"So?" said Lucy.

Liz shook her head. "Nothing. Just a feeling." She refocused on Grabber. "Well, young dragon. We have got to stop your robbing ways. I think you're going to have to spend quite a lot of time in the Dragons' Den with—"

Liz broke off suddenly hearing a loud hooter, an even louder clang, and an even louder holler of pain from outside.

They rushed out to find Henry Bacon sitting on his back door step, holding a hand to his head. There was an egg-shaped bump on it.

"Henry? What happened?" asked Liz.

"Bacon's patent alarm system," he grimaced, pointing to the frying pan dangling on a piece of string above his head. "Set off by an intruder. Delayed reaction from the frying pan. Clonked me instead of the villain."

Lucy was about to burst out laughing, when she saw something looking at her from across the garden. Something with big round frightened eyes, hiding underneath Mr Bacon's garden bench. "Hhh! Could it have been…that?" she said. She looked at her mother, then pointed to the bench.

Liz walked to the bench and dragged the 'something' out.

It was a young tabby cat. Around its neck was a paper collar. On the collar was some writing. It said, "My name is Bingo. Please give me a home."

"*Bingo?*" said Liz.

And the cat looked up at her — and purred.

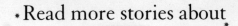

Read more stories about

The Dragons of Wayward Crescent

GRUFFEN

978 1 40830 232 3 £8.99 (hb)
978 1 84616 609 9 £4.99 (pbk)

GAUGE

978 1 40830 233 0 £8.99 (hb)
978 1 84616 610 5 £4.99 (pbk)

GLADE

978 1 40830 234 7 £8.99 (hb)
978 1 84616 611 2 £4.99 (pbk)